The MORGAN HORSE
COLORING BOOK

**Photographs of Beautiful Morgan Horses
Magically Transformed into Coloring Book Images**

Visit Willow Bend Publishing to see some of the original photographs of the Morgans in this coloring book, as well as to discover other exciting books about horses.
www.willowbendpublishing.com

Copyright © 2021 by Ellen F. Feld

Published by Willow Bend Publishing

All rights reserved, including the right of reproduction in part or in whole in any form.

Cover photograph by Genevieve Kerr
Book design by Creative Publishing Book Design

Library of Congress Catalog Card Number: 2021917354

ISBN: 978-1-7337674-4-6

Direct inquiries to: Willow Bend Publishing
P.O. Box 304
Goshen, MA 01032
www.willowbendpublishing.com

Printed in the United States of America

Young colts CG (left) and Pep (right) are
best friends who love to play.

Lumi (foal) meets Smore, an Australian
shepherd, for the first time.

This rooster loves to show off.
(from *Shadow: The Curious Morgan Horse*)

Annie (left) and Rimfire (right) are at
the gate, waiting for dinner.

Annie plays in her pasture.
(book cover of *Annie: The Mysterious Morgan Horse*)

A horse runs through a field.

(from *Blackjack: The Magical Morgan Horse*)

Frosty (left) and her daughter Annie (right)
out on the trail.

What's so funny, Annie?

Shadow plays with a butterfly.
(from *Shadow: The Curious Morgan Horse*)

Annie trotting through her pasture.

Blackjack shows off his championship ribbon.
(book cover of *Blackjack: The Champion Morgan Horse*)

Shadow meets a deer.
(from *Shadow: The Curious Morgan Horse*)

Blackjack enjoying a summer day.

Blackjack has his Santa cap on
and is ready for the holidays.

Shadow meets a skunk.
(from *Shadow: The Curious Morgan Horse*)

Blackjack runs through a field with his
championship ribbon and neck sash.

Beau soars over a jump.

Shadow and her new friend Willow the basset hound.
(back cover of *Shadow: The Curious Morgan Horse*)

Tommy has his holiday outfit on
and he's ready to celebrate!

Raine will sit down on command – what a smart horse!

Mr. Skunk wanders through the woods.
(from *Shadow: The Curious Morgan Horse*)

Donkey-Donk, who lives on a farm with lots
of Morgans, loves to wear t-shirts.

Billy looks gorgeous in his western show bridle.

Willow is a lovable basset hound.
(from *Shadow: The Curious Morgan Horse*)

Junior looks beautiful with a blue ribbon
hanging from his bridle!

Frosty and her foal Skittles trot around the pasture.

Holly wants a horse and dreams about them every night. Will Pegasus be in her dream tonight?
(from *Blackjack: The Magical Morgan Horse*)

Magic and her foal Cappy scratch each other's backs.

Frosty loves to laugh!

A very fluffy pony from Holly's dreams.
(from *Blackjack: The Magical Morgan Horse*)

Frosty peeks through her stall window.

Chrome and his rider navigate through some
giant balls at a trail competition.

A colorful butterfly flutters around some flowers.
(from *Shadow: The Curious Morgan Horse*)

Take Our Picture! Hannah and her foal
Pebbles pose for a photograph.

Andy plays with his favorite toy – a horse ball!

Frosty frantically calls out for her foal Shadow.

(from *Shadow: The Curious Morgan Horse*)

Pedey is ready for a nap.

Entry checks out her long legs as she
zooms around her pasture.

Three of the horses from Holly's dreams.
(from *Blackjack: The Magical Morgan Horse*)

May I have a treat? Robin loves to bow every time she hears
the crinkle of the treat bag, hopeful she'll get a horse cookie.

Luna takes her rider safely through a pond.

A high-trotting horse from Holly's dreams.
(from *Blackjack: The Magical Morgan Horse*)

Rusty and Heather fly over a jump.
(front cover of *Rusty: The High-Flying Morgan Horse*)

Rimfire zooms around a barrel.
(front cover of *Rimfire: The Barrel Racing Morgan Horse*)

Frosty and her foal Shadow run through a field.
(from *Shadow: The Curious Morgan Horse*)

Robin playfully jumps into the air.
(front cover of *Robin: The Lovable Morgan Horse*)

Freddie charges toward the camera.

Justin Morgan was the very first Morgan.
(from *Justin Morgan and the Big Horse Race*)

Floyd loves playing with his giant ball.

Shadow makes a new friend.
(front cover of *Shadow: The Curious Morgan Horse*)

Justin Morgan is such a pretty horse.
(from *Justin Morgan and the Big Horse Race*)

Muddy takes a bow – a very talented Morgan!

Lady is a beautiful Morgan filly who
can't wait to hit the show ring.

Justin Morgan trotting around the farm.
(from *Justin Morgan and the Big Horse Race*)

Blackjack strikes a show pose in front of the
statue of Justin Morgan at the UVM Morgan
Horse Farm in Weybridge, Vermont.

Viper has a new toy – connect the dots to see what it is.

Justin Morgan plays in his field.
Can you find the bunny and the chicken?

Felix and his rider dash through a field at
a mounted archery competition.

Seven and his rider Steve enjoy a stroll
through a lake on a hot summer day.

An adorable pinto pony from Holly's dreams.
(from *Blackjack: The Magical Morgan Horse*)

Scott and his horse Cabo perform at a circus.

Bugs! Go Back!

Lost Shoe! Go Back!

Blackjack lost his blue ribbon!
Can you help him find it?